LOOK AND FIND®
the AMAZING SPIDER-MAN®

LAYOUT ARTIST/ILLUSTRATION COORDINATOR: HOWARD BENDER
PENCILERS: HOWARD BENDER, RICH YANIZESKI, BRIAN CLOPPER, ALEX MORRISSEY, BRIAN BUNIAK
INKERS: DON HECK, MIKE ESPOSITO, MARIE SEVERIN
COLORISTS: NANSI HOOLAHAN, BRIAN BUNIAK, KEN FEDUNIEWICZ, TOM LUTH, TOM ZIUKO
COVER ARTIST: JEFF ALBRECHT STUDIOS

ILLUSTRATION SCRIPT DEVELOPMENT BY DWIGHT ZIMMERMAN

PUBLISHED BY
LOUIS WEBER, C.E.O.
PUBLICATIONS INTERNATIONAL, LTD.
7373 NORTH CICERO AVENUE
LINCOLNWOOD, ILLINOIS 60712

WWW.PILBOOKS.COM

ISBN 1-4127-0370-0

publications international, ltd.

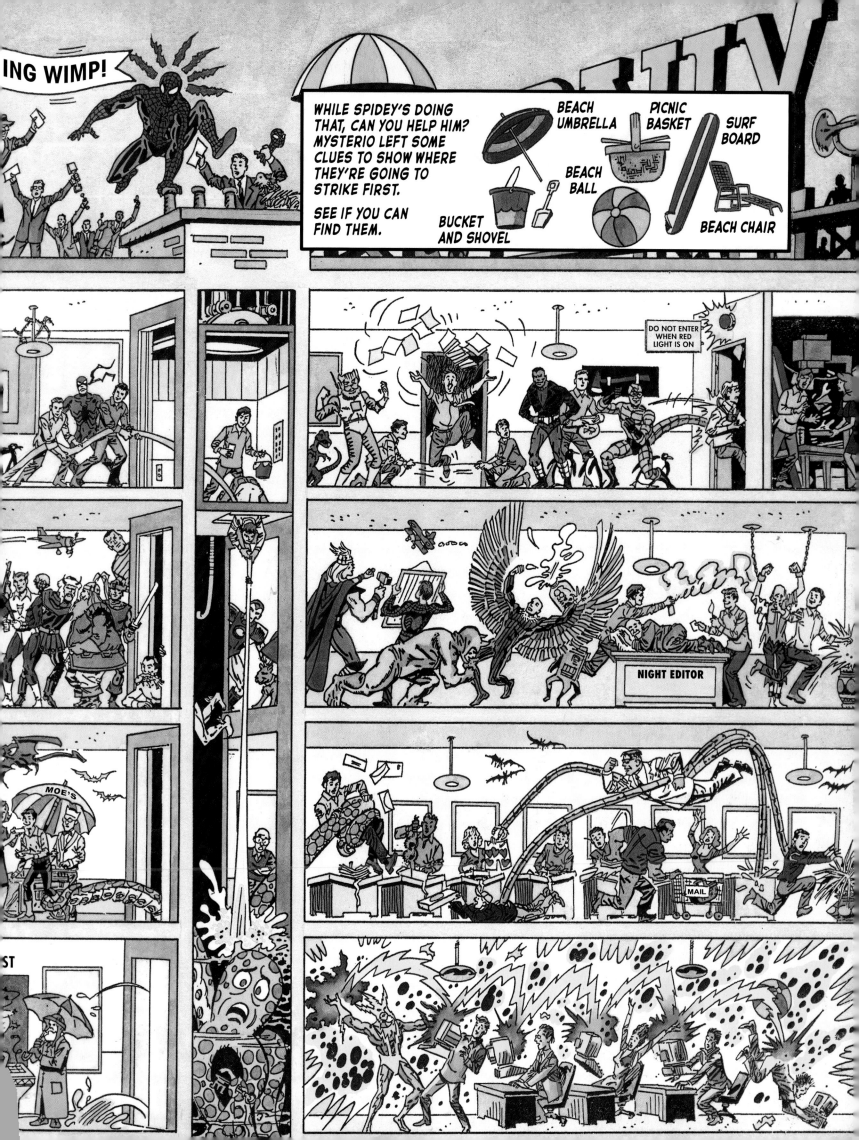

WHILE SPIDEY'S WORKING ON HIS PLAN, SEE IF YOU CAN FIND THESE THINGS THAT TELL WHERE MYSTERIO WILL GO FROM HERE.

THEATER MASKS

ACTOR

ACTRESS

COWBOY WITH LASSO

OPERA GLASSES

LION

TAXI

I SHOULD HAVE GUESSED THAT MYSTERIO WOULD END UP IN THE TIMES SQUARE THEATER DISTRICT. HE PROBABLY FEELS RIGHT AT HOME HERE. IF ONLY I CAN SLIP A SPIDER TRACER ON HIM. THEN I'LL BE ABLE TO FOLLOW HIM ANYWHERE—EVEN TO HIS SECRET HIDEOUT.

SPIDEY IS RELYING ON HIS SPIDER TRACER TO FOLLOW MYSTERIO. SINCE YOU DON'T HAVE ONE, SEE IF YOU CAN FIND THESE CLUES THAT TELL WHERE HIS SECRET HIDEOUT IS.

WOODEN PALLET

CRATE

BARREL

HARD HAT

FORKLIFT

DOLLY

IF SPIDEY CAN FIND THESE ITEMS, HE'LL HAVE AN IDEA WHERE TO GO FROM HERE. SEE IF YOU CAN FIND THEM AND FIND THE REAL SPIDEY, TOO!

TYPEWRITER

TELEPHONE

CAMERA

PENCIL & NOTEPAD

TAPE RECORDER

NEWSPAPER

I HAD TO CALL IN A LOT OF DEBTS, BUT I'VE GOT SOME OLD FRIENDS HELPING ME OUT NOW. EVEN AFTER WE GET ALL THESE BAD GUYS UNDER CONTROL, THE WORK WON'T BE DONE. MYSTERIO HAS PLANTED EIGHT BOMBS IN THE CITY STREETS. WE HAVE TO FIND THEM, OR THERE'S NO TELLING HOW MANY PEOPLE WILL BE HURT!

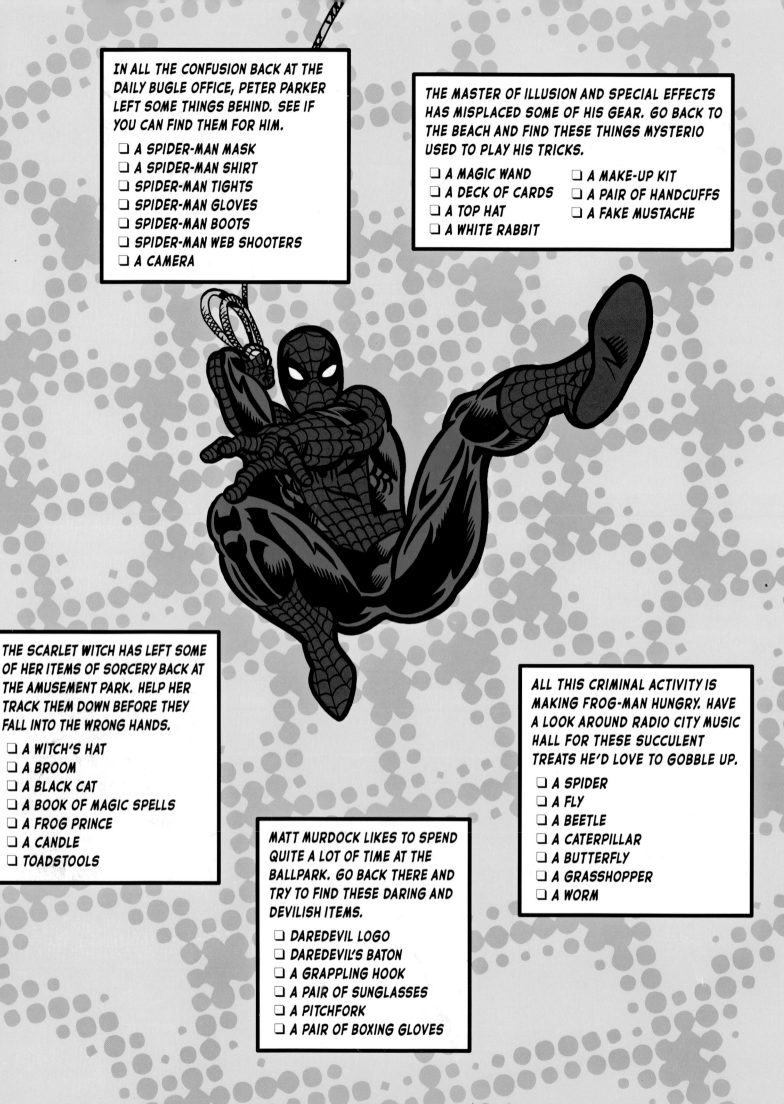

IN ALL THE CONFUSION BACK AT THE DAILY BUGLE OFFICE, PETER PARKER LEFT SOME THINGS BEHIND. SEE IF YOU CAN FIND THEM FOR HIM.

- ❏ A SPIDER-MAN MASK
- ❏ A SPIDER-MAN SHIRT
- ❏ SPIDER-MAN TIGHTS
- ❏ SPIDER-MAN GLOVES
- ❏ SPIDER-MAN BOOTS
- ❏ SPIDER-MAN WEB SHOOTERS
- ❏ A CAMERA

THE MASTER OF ILLUSION AND SPECIAL EFFECTS HAS MISPLACED SOME OF HIS GEAR. GO BACK TO THE BEACH AND FIND THESE THINGS MYSTERIO USED TO PLAY HIS TRICKS.

- ❏ A MAGIC WAND
- ❏ A DECK OF CARDS
- ❏ A TOP HAT
- ❏ A WHITE RABBIT
- ❏ A MAKE-UP KIT
- ❏ A PAIR OF HANDCUFFS
- ❏ A FAKE MUSTACHE

THE SCARLET WITCH HAS LEFT SOME OF HER ITEMS OF SORCERY BACK AT THE AMUSEMENT PARK. HELP HER TRACK THEM DOWN BEFORE THEY FALL INTO THE WRONG HANDS.

- ❏ A WITCH'S HAT
- ❏ A BROOM
- ❏ A BLACK CAT
- ❏ A BOOK OF MAGIC SPELLS
- ❏ A FROG PRINCE
- ❏ A CANDLE
- ❏ TOADSTOOLS

MATT MURDOCK LIKES TO SPEND QUITE A LOT OF TIME AT THE BALLPARK. GO BACK THERE AND TRY TO FIND THESE DARING AND DEVILISH ITEMS.

- ❏ DAREDEVIL LOGO
- ❏ DAREDEVIL'S BATON
- ❏ A GRAPPLING HOOK
- ❏ A PAIR OF SUNGLASSES
- ❏ A PITCHFORK
- ❏ A PAIR OF BOXING GLOVES

ALL THIS CRIMINAL ACTIVITY IS MAKING FROG-MAN HUNGRY. HAVE A LOOK AROUND RADIO CITY MUSIC HALL FOR THESE SUCCULENT TREATS HE'D LOVE TO GOBBLE UP.

- ❏ A SPIDER
- ❏ A FLY
- ❏ A BEETLE
- ❏ A CATERPILLAR
- ❏ A BUTTERFLY
- ❏ A GRASSHOPPER
- ❏ A WORM